COLOUR ME
GIRL CRUSH

First published in the United Kingdom in 2014 by
Portico Books
10 Southcombe Street
London
W14 0RA

An imprint of Anova Books Company Ltd

ISBN 9781909396579

A CIP catalogue record for this book is available from the British Library.

10 9 8 7 6 5 4 3 2 1

Printed and bound by 1010 Printing International Ltd, China

This book can be ordered direct from the publisher at
www.anovabooks.com

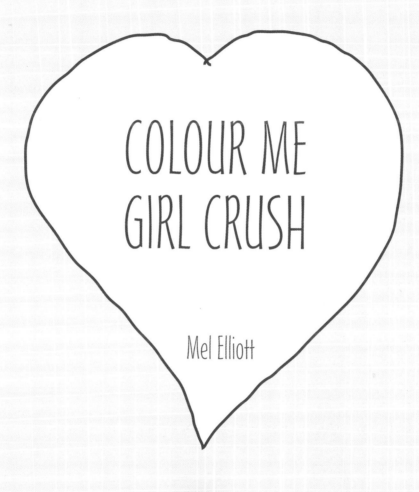

COLOUR ME GIRL CRUSH

Mel Elliott

PORTICO

CONTENTS

MEL'S HALL OF FEMME

We once lived in an era where it was the law for women to hate each other. We would flick through magazines raging with venomous jealousy and saying things like, "I don't know WHAT Luke Perry SEES in her! LOOK! She has a hair out of place and like, oh my god, she is so FAKE!"

Luckily though, we woke up, realised that we are not in *Mean Girls* and we now live in an age where women are allowed to like one another. We would rather appreciate other women *for* their flaws, rather than ridicule them.

That makes sense, right?

There may still be some pangs of jealousy. It's perfectly okay to "want her bum" or appreciate someone's toned arms, wobbly tummy or voluminous hair …

LET'S CELEBRATE FEMALE SOLIDARITY!

And what better way to celebrate than with a packet of felt tips!

So, colouring pens at the ready, let's colour in our favourite girl crushes, from the kooky, the funny, the stylish and the brainy to the downright sexy.

Let's appreciate women of all shapes and sizes for their individuality, their bravery, their style, their hair or their ability to entertain us while still being completely gorgeous.

Feel free to embrace the stylist in you too! Add patterns to dresses, bows to hair and go crazy on the make-up. Most of all, have fun and colour them good.

Love,

Mel

x

For my daughter Pearl, my mum Linda, my grandma Doris, my sister Nanette and all the other wonderful women and girls who have enhanced my life.

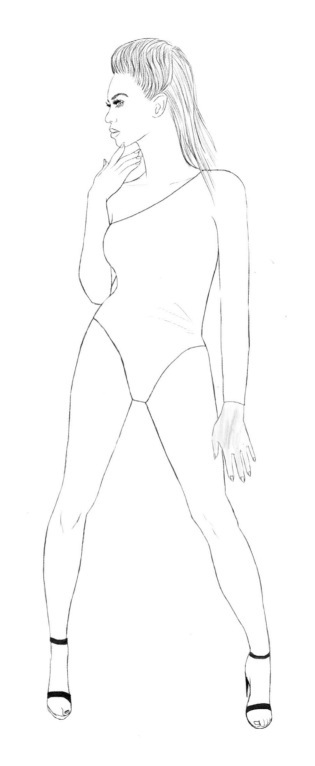

BEYONCÉ

Please let me be Beyoncé
I swear I'll work out every day
I'll worship Jesus and I'll pray
I'll learn to knit and crochet
I'll pull orphans around in the snow on a sleigh
I'll rehome any poor dogs that are stray
I'll learn to cook the perfect soufflé
And stop eating crap, greasy take-away
I'll find out the way to San José
and not eat sweets and get tooth decay
I'll do crafts with my kids like papier-maché
and take them to swimming or tap or ballet
I will never lead anyone else astray
And all life's rules I will strictly obey
If I could just be Beyoncé
Like, just for a week, so what do you say?

You don't have to score Beyoncé out of ten, I did it for you …

JENNIFER LAWRENCE

This may be the ultimate girl next door … Quirky, sarcastic, and … clumsy in a huge dress. We love Jen for the way she seems so real compared to many stars. But the star-factor shines through anyway: this is a girl who deliberately goes to big bashes with no make-up and still looks heart-stoppingly gorgeous. Just not fair.

Perhaps it shouldn't be a surprise: one of her best-known roles on screen has been a woman with no make-up, and usually in a mess from fighting for her life! In *The Hunger Games* she is too busy being epic at shooting things with a bow and arrow to sit around feeling like a damsel in distress … In fact that's the man's job in this film!

Hunger is apparently on Jennifer's mind as well: she champions eating properly and has no interest in starving herself for roles … Of the many quotes floating around the Internet, I think my favourite is the one where she says "I eat like a caveman"! I think we should all go and get a slice of cake now in celebration of how awesome Jennifer Lawrence is. And then maybe take up archery lessons to burn off the calories.

Jennifer scores

ALEXA CHUNG

Alexa is one of the coolest kids on the block and she hangs around with all the other cool kids to prove it. Her style is so understated and effortless that it's easy to believe that she actually wakes up looking this cool (maybe she does! How depressing is that!?).

With "don't care" hair, minimal make-up and a style that equates to:
Grown-up schoolgirl + tomboy x Chanel = Alexa

Alexa is so cool that Mulberry even named a bag after her!

If Mulberry named a bag after YOU, what would it look like?

/10

Alexa gets an effortless

MICHELLE WILLIAMS

There are plenty of actresses in *Girl Crush* but I think that Michelle Williams is one of the best. Her performance in *Blue Valentine* left me emotionally exhausted (and yes, I have forgiven her for snogging Ryan Gosling) and her portrayal of Marilyn Monroe in *My Week With Marilyn* made me completely forget I was watching Michelle Williams and not Norma Jean herself.

However, one of the BEST things about Michelle Williams, is her hair. She has the best hair since Meg Ryan circa 1994. It was straight after drawing the image opposite that I went to my hairdresser and said I wanted my hair like Michelle Williams. I left the salon looking less like Michelle Williams and more like Elliott from *E.T.*, but you can't have everything, and anyway, I used to think the kid in *E.T.* was really cute.

Michelle scores / 10

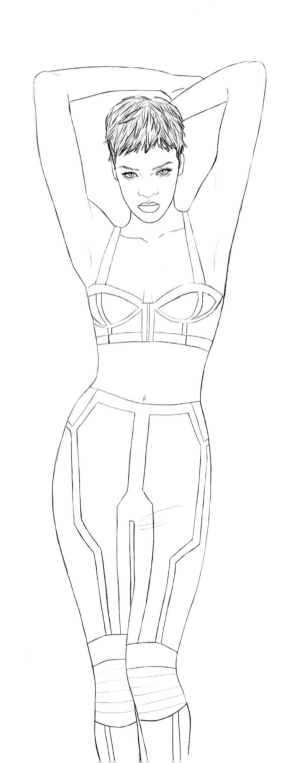

RIHANNA

She's the good girl that turned bad
With outfits that are rad
All men they want to snog her
Your brother, your uncle, your dad

But if they want to be her fella
They'll need an umbrella
and when she's on a high
She's like a diamond that is stellar

Her costumes are revealing
But her body's quite appealing
and her performances are mega
as she sings with passion and feeling

With a truly outrageous manner
Some stations want to ban her
But whatever she does or thinks or says
We love that girl Rihanna

Rihanna scores

10

LANA DEL REY

If you had blanked all pop culture from the moment you were born, you may be forgiven for thinking Lana Del Ray was a singer of long ago: from her looks to the tweaking on her publicity shots and album covers, everything about her says "vintage" and "retro" and also "kind of scary". With her sometimes smoky voice and the sultry glower in her photos, she's making a big stand against any sort of "pop" labelling, even before you hear her music.

Though she's only stomped onto the music scene recently, her fantastic retro look has already captured peoples' imagination, and she is why everyone is wearing vivid lipstick and huge bundles of flowers in their hair. And she's already had a Mulberry bag named after her.

I'd be lucky to have a bag of crisps named after me!

Lana scores

KATE MOSS

How awesome we all thought we looked in our boot-cut jeans, sashaying around like Monica from *Friends* and playing "snake" on our mobile phones. That was until Kate Moss showed up in some magazine wearing a pair of skinny jeans.

This was 2002 and over a decade later we're still mad for skinnies. If Kate Moss hadn't worn her grey "Superfines" all those years ago, would we still be walking around with cowboy legs? I dread to think!

The reason skinnies made such a huge impact on us was that Kate Moss wore them and created a fashion revolution. She is also the reason that girls started wearing wellies on Kensington High Street, but I'll forgive her for that.

Kate is the world's best-loved supermodel, and while we know we won't look as good as her in our skinnies, we want to give it a damned good try.

Kate scores a trend-setting **/10**

LENA DUNHAM

When I heard about *Girls* I assumed it was going to be another *Sex And The City*, and as brilliant as *SATC* was, we're kind of over that. The fact that the characters in *Girls* are younger than me also had me assuming I wouldn't relate to it, and so when I sat down to the first episode, for me it had already failed.

But how wrong I was.

Lena Dunham's creation is so fresh, so real and SO relatable that men and women of all ages lap it up.

The four lead characters represent an astounding observation of women, each one flawed to the brim but oozing charisma, and making us (and our problems) feel like we'd easily fit into their gang.

Hannah, played by Lena Dunham, has an awkward style with nothing fitting quite right, but whether she is wearing patterned blouses, short playsuits or babydoll dresses, she always looks really cute.

I remember my Mum always telling me not to use my pockets and that they were sewn up so that they wouldn't spoil the shape of the clothes. "So what's the point in them being there at all?" I would ask. Hannah uses her pockets ... and so do I, it saves money on handbags and mittens.

Lena scores 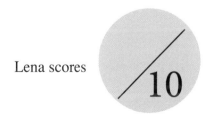 /10

Zosia Mamet AKA "Shoshanna"

Lena Dunham AKA "Hannah"

Allison Williams AKA "Marnie"

Jemima Kirke AKA "Jessa"

Try to match the "Girls" characters to their item of clothing

ROM-COM SPECIAL

From Lucille Ball and Doris Day, to Kristen Wiig and Emma Stone, some women are just great at making us LOL and ROFL ... while still looking completely drop-dead gorgeous.

My rom-com special celebrates seven leading ladies (Meg Ryan, Julia Roberts, Renée Zellwegger, Mila Kunis, Sandra Bullock, Reese Witherspoon and Drew Barrymore), each one having delighted us in the rom-com genre.

MEG RYAN

Sleepless in Seattle
You've Got Mail
When Harry Met Sally
French Kiss

10

JULIA ROBERTS

Pretty Woman
Runaway Bride
Notting Hill
My Best Friend's Wedding

/10

RENÉE ZELLWEGER

Bridget Jones's Diary
Bridget Jones: The Edge of Reason
Jerry McGuire
New in Town
Down with Love

/10

SANDRA BULLOCK

Miss Congeniality
Speed
While You Were Sleeping
The Proposal
Two Weeks Notice

/10

MILA KUNIS

Friends with Benefits
Date Night
Forgetting Sarah Marshall
Tony & Tina's Wedding

/10

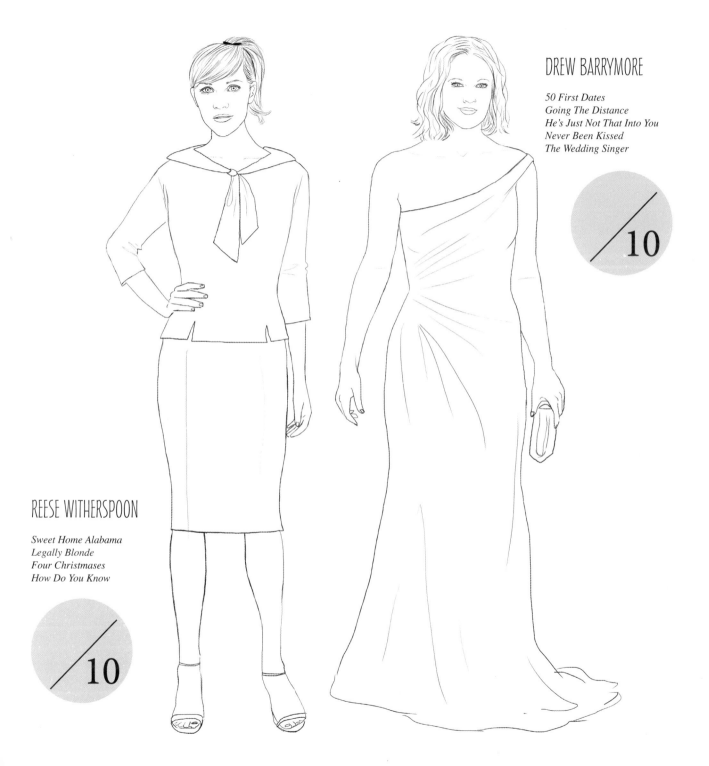

DREW BARRYMORE

50 First Dates
Going The Distance
He's Just Not That Into You
Never Been Kissed
The Wedding Singer

/10

REESE WITHERSPOON

Sweet Home Alabama
Legally Blonde
Four Christmases
How Do You Know

/10

EMMA STONE

Oh Emma, won't you be my new best friend? I could braid your hair and we could stay up all night talking about stuff … She's the girl next door with the freckles and the ginger hair. And the husky voice. Did I mention the husky voice? She has that vibe as she laughs and jokes through her interviews, which just says she would be great to hang out with and gossip.

As one of the stars of the epic rom-com *Crazy, Stupid, Love,* we, well I, fell in love with her as the awkward but gorgeous Hannah, who utters the immortal line to Ryan Gosling's character with something bordering on horror: "It's like you're Photoshopped!"… I think that's still composed compared to how I might be in that situation!

Her style is casual, fun and colourful and somehow she always looks flawless whatever she wears. Her hair can be red, blonde or brunette, and each colour she matches well and pulls it off.

Emma scores a very cute /10

CARA DELEVINGNE

Cara Delevingne makes us all go green
With envy as we witness the best eyebrows we have seen!

She struts her stuff for Burberry, Gucci, Prada and Preen
The front row sit in awe as she lowers their self-esteem

Her face is animated, she's every photographer's dream
Her pout is like a pillow, her smile like a laser beam

Magazines united, one thing they're all agreeing
CARA IS A MEGA-GORGEOUS SUPER HUMAN BEING!

Cara gets a mega-gorgeous /10

EMMA WATSON

There has been a moment where I think every girl has looked in the mirror and tried to imagine how cute they would look with a pixie cut, and that was when we first saw Emma Watson after she shed her Hermione skin and stepped out as a fey, leggy butterfly. I think most of us decided we would not look half as cute as she did and sensibly put down the scissors.

Emma's got an eye for startling red-carpet style as well: no one could have thought she was a child actor any more when she strutted her stuff wearing a thin lace dress with a short skirt made of sleek black feathers resembling raven's wings ... Very witchy, and very mature! I'm not sure what charm she used to keep her legs warm when she was wearing it, but it made me think she might be magic after all ...

I had a quick go at making up my own *Harry Potter* spell she might have used to become a stylish star ... Wave your wand and say "Stella Nitidus!"*

Emma gets

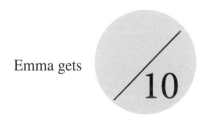

10

* Can't promise any magic will happen if you never got your Hogwarts letter.

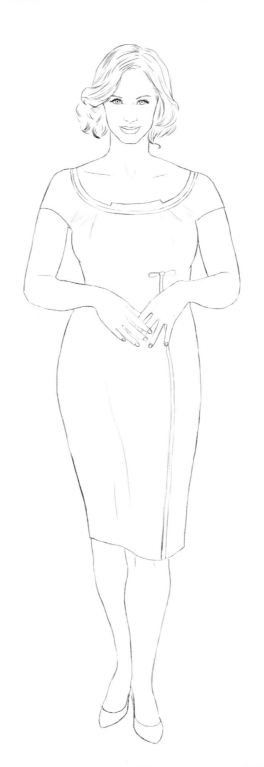

CHRISTINA HENDRICKS

Mad Men's style seems to come from one figurehead: the curvaceous Joan, AKA Christina Hendricks, in what has become her stand-out role. The Queen Bee of a hive of pretty secretaries, the bold '60s fashion promoted by the historical advertising drama is prominently worn by Christina. With striking red hair and the perfect hourglass figure, it's hard to look at anything else when she's on screen!

In the show she wears a range of knee-length, colourful dresses and suit-skirts, or tight pencil skirts with loose silk shirts, usually matched with a flawless up-do. Perhaps the most interesting piece of TV jewellery at the moment is the long necklace Joan wears with a pen as a … pendant. I'm sorry. Anyway, it's a fantastic piece and even has a practical use, a great symbol of a character who can get things done in her office! If you love the retro look, now is probably the time to sit down with a box set of this show …

Christina Hendricks gets a voluptuous

10

JULIANNE MOORE

In *A Single Man*, set in the swinging '60s, Julianne Moore plays …
the BFF of a delicious yet saddened gay man played by Colin Firth.

Okay, we've all done it. Had a few girly cocktails and then
attempted make-up application before hitting the town – but never ever
have I done it with such style and panache as Julianne Moore in this film.

With a gin in one hand she applies perfect eyeliner and then sashays
around swigging and mumbling and generally being just like I aim to be
when my children leave home (and with all the same furntiture to bump
into too).

If I can look and be anything like Julianne Moore in this film one day,
I'll be a very happy woman (well, happy in a "high on alcohol, posh
cigarettes and a fabulous wardrobe" kind of way).

I give Julianne Moore 10

NATALIE PORTMAN

Natalie is famously one of the more intellectual Hollywood stars of our times, and mixed with her elegance and a beauty that has drawn comparisons to Audrey Hepburn, this is one almost supernaturally perfect lady. The comparisons to Audrey have come all through her career: once she even got to pose in the actual dress from *Breakfast at Tiffany's*! Her photo shoots and red carpet style are classic and timeless.

In one of my favourite films, *Closer*, Natalie plays the vulnerable Alice and completely holds her own against Jude Law and Julia Roberts.

A life-long dancer, she put her flexibility literally to the test with the gothic ballet horror *Black Swan*. She has also happily proved that she is one of those women who looks good shaved bald and dressed in a sack, as seen in *V for Vendetta* … Now there's a hard look for the rest of us girls to pull off! Anyone planning to marathon this actress's back catalogue should come armed with a cushion to hug and a mug of hot chocolate to steady the nerves.

Natalie scores a sophisticated /10

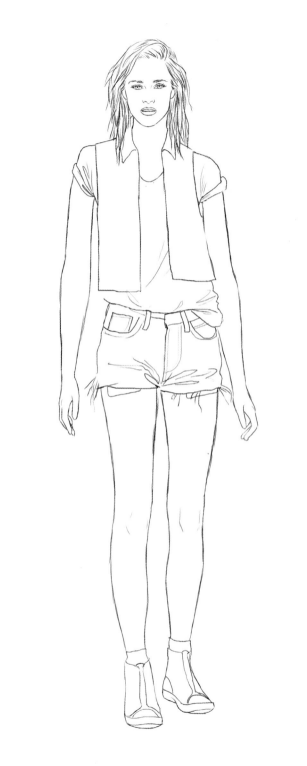

KRISTEN STEWART

It's the perfectly cast actress for Miss "Beautiful Swan" Bella from *Twilight* … Tousled-haired Kristen is well-known for her pouty, cool attitude and reluctance to smile on camera, perfect for the vampire-romance movie. While Bella wears a range of comfortable (and, importantly, warm, considering the icy hunk Edward she spends the film series sighing over) indie clothes, Kristen Stewart has an edgier look that is decidedly punky.

She often is seen wearing band T-shirts and she has a history with punk and rock: she played Joan Jett in *The Runaways*, a much wilder character than the one most people associate with her, but perhaps closer to Kristen's heart. She can play the guitar and sing, doing so for that film, and these days she sports a few punk tattoos. She looks a great deal more comfortable in the shots of her out and about in her normal garb than she does in her dresses for premières and award ceremonies!

Kristen scores

10

ANNA WINTOUR

Anna Wintour is the English editor-in-chief of American *Vogue*, as well as being art director of its publisher, Condé Nast.

However, she is best known for sitting in the front row at fashion shows, sporting dark glasses and a facial expression that gives nothing away. She is often seen surrounded by A-listers, all looking deeply terrified and desperate to be liked by her.

Anna scores  /10

GRACE CODDINGTON

Grace Coddington is often seen alongside Anna Wintour as she is American *Vogue*'s creative director.

The former model and crazy-haired beauty couldn't be more different to Anna, often sporting mannish coats and a big smile.

Grace scores /10

GWEN STEFANI

Picture the scene ... Gwen Stefani is sitting alone in a stinky dressing gown, sobbing because some guy said they'd call and they didn't, or because some dude dumped her because she was too opinionated or something.

Difficult isn't it? That's because Gwen Stefani is a TOUGH GIRL! She'd take it on the chin and go have some fun!

I remember hearing "Don't Speak" for the first time on the radio and thinking it was great. It was some days later that I managed to *see* Gwen and, like most people, totally ignored the rest of the band that was No Doubt.

WHAT A BABE! With her navy polka-dot dress (which she wore with no shoes OR socks) and with her '50s glamour hairdo teamed with punkesque clothing, it's no doubt that Gwen started the vintage/retro fashion revolution that is so big today. All of a sudden, vintage became less "twee" and more "twough"!

It wasn't too long before Gwen Stefani's style needed its own label, and so L.A.M.B. was born and showcased in her video for "What You Waiting For?", as seen in the image opposite.

Gwen gets 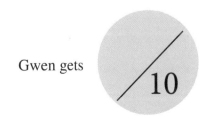 10

FAMILY SPECIAL

DAKOTA & ELLE FANNING

These adorable blonde actresses have been in showbiz for almost their whole lives. Elle has been appearing as young versions of Dakota's characters for their whole career, but she's now the taller one of the two!

GOLDIE HAWN & KATE HUDSON

A glamorous mother and daughter pairing. Appearing in red carpet shots together, you can see the family resemblance at work. They both seem to have a great time when they are together, laughing and playing around … Enjoying your family's company is very important!

MARY-KATE & ASHLEY OLSEN

Acting almost from birth (if being held while on screen counts as acting!), these superstar twins are nearly impossible to tell apart when one of them isn't dyeing her hair another colour! They have retired from acting for the time being and are focusing their energy on being fashion designers.

LENNON & MAISY

Adorable as he is, I never thought I'd have much in common with Harry Styles, but it turns out that Stylesy and me share a love of Canadian child country-singing sister duo Lennon and Maisy. Do check them out on YouTube or TV show *Nashville*, if you haven't already!

LENNON and MAISY

AUDREY TAUTOU

Everyone named "Audrey" is adorable. FACT.

I love Audrey Tautou and have watched most of her films. The reason I love Audrey Tautou is that she is French. Which means that, more often than not, she is in French films, which means that, more often than not, they are subtitled ... and I LOVE subtitled films.

The reason that I love subtitled films is that (A) everyone else in my house hates subtitled films so I get to watch them alone, and (B) since my early 20s, due to a bone disease in my inner ears, I am partially deaf. Subtitled films let me, with the soundtrack faintly in the background, read the wonderful scripts, watch the wonderful expressions on the actors' faces and enjoy the films utterly and completely (which is very difficult to do otherwise).

It's only when you watch films in this way that you truly appreciate facial expressions, subtle eye movements, the way someone walks, smiles or frowns, and Audrey Tautou has an incredibly expressive face.

In *Amélie* Audrey is totally adorable, but please try some of her "proper" French films*, turn the sound down really low and experience her true beauty like I do.

I give Audrey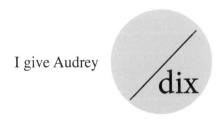

* Try *Delicacy* and *Priceless* for starters.

KATY PERRY

Whoever said "less is more" obviously forgot to send Katy Perry the memo. And, you know what? I'm glad Katy didn't get the memo.

Who doesn't want to run around all day wearing sequins and glitter and tiger suits and bras that look like giant cup-cakes, and sing and shout and dance and ROAR!?

You don't? How about if you were five years old?

Being very good at something doesn't automatically mean that you have to take yourself and your profession too seriously – I should know!

Stay crazy, Katy!

Katy gets a roaring

10

ZOOEY DESCHANEL

When I asked my Twitter and Facebook friends for their thoughts on who to put in *Girl Crush*, Zooey Deschanel's name popped up time after time.

Once labelled "the cutest girl in the world", Zooey Deschanel made quite an impression with her small role in *Almost Famous* in 2000. The world got wind of her quirky style which, during the era of Paris Hilton, was quite the antidote. Being somewhat different to the leggy blonde film stars we had previously been used to, Zooey found fame as the "indie chic" girl, with her role in *500 Days of Summer* being the perfect platform.

Her hit TV show *New Girl* is in its third season and features Jess, a young woman who shares a flat with three single men following a bad break-up. Zooey sings the theme tune, and in my opinion, Zooey's indie-folk band, She and Him, is responsible for one of the loveliest Christmas albums of all time.*

Zooey gets

/10

* *A Very She and Him Christmas*, 2011

TINA FEY

This current queen of American comedy is making it big with her own show, *30 Rock*. And she's helping make glasses cool again!

Tina Fey is lovely to behold, hilarious to watch, and not afraid to lampoon the biggest names. A *Saturday Night Live* regular, the videos of her impersonating Sarah Palin went viral, and we loved her impression so much that some of the quotes from her skit were mistakenly attributed to the real politician!

Her iconic character from *30 Rock*, Liz Lemon, is a fantastically awkward woman who isn't afraid to make a fool of herself, and Tina embraces the character, having a world of fun with her.

What would your alliterative fruit-based surname be?

I'd be Mel Melon.

I award Tina 10

MADONNA

Madonna's self-titled album, from way back in 1983, features some of the best pop songs EVER*. Grown-ups everywhere were shocked, horrified and stunned that this woman was parading round with her underwear on display, believing that, if you can see a woman's bra strap, she may as well be completely starkers.

Madonna didn't listen though, her undergarments continued to display themselves, and she has since challenged audiences year after year, decade after decade, with musical innovation and fashion bravery. Madonna is probably the most influential female pop star to date, with many of her contemporaries emulating her, many perhaps without even realising it!

Madonna scores 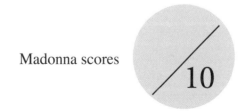 10

* "Borderline", "Holiday", "Lucky Star", "Get Into the Groove"

ROCK GODDESS SPECIAL

Debbie Harry

If I could look like any woman in this book, it would be Debbie Harry circa 1980 (although she looks fantastic these days too!).

The former Playboy Bunny is best known for being the lead singer of Blondie, who pioneered the American new-wave music scene.

Best Moments:
"One Way or Another" 1978
"Rapture" 1980
"Picture This" 1978
"In the Flesh" 1976

10

Stevie Nicks

Stevie Nicks is best known for her work with American rock group Fleetwood Mac, but her solo career more than stands up for itself too.

Best Moments:
"Landslide" 1975 (FM)
"Edge of Seventeen" 1982 (SN)
"Rhiannon" 1976 (FM)
"Big Love" 1987 (FM)
"Landslide" 1978 (FM)
"Rooms on Fire" 1989 (SN)

/10

LITTLE MIX

First *The X Factor* UK gave us One Direction, then in 2011, for the first time ever, a band won the contest in the form of Little Mix!

They consist of (from left to right): Jessy Nelson, Leigh-Anne Pinnock, Jade Thirwall and Perrie Edwards, and it was no surprise that they won.

In the days of female *X Factor* contestants trying desperately to out-ballad one another, Little Mix were such a feisty and refreshing change. They perform with perfect pop aplomb, with great singing, fun rapping and a sassy stage presence.

Long live Little Mix!

I give Little Mix
a poptastic

10

LADY GAGA

Lady Gaga (or Stefani Germanotta as she used to be) has oodles of stage presence, mostly dictated by the oodles of weird costumes she comes up with. There can't be a dull moment with her around. However fantastic she may look, there is a line where fans are unlikely to incorporate strips of bacon into their everyday style. Nevertheless, as a walking art piece or modern icon, no one can come close to this Lady. And we haven't even got to her music and her fantastic voice, which is as powerful as she is wacky …

Quick game: what is the nearest item to your left? Staple a hundred of them together and you have yourself your very own Gaga-style dress! Nothing is beyond the realm of possibility, which is why she is just so fun to follow, and always seems to make headlines.

I give Lady Gaga

10

LINDSEY WIXON

SCARLETT JOHANSSON

ANGELINA JOLIE

I WANT HER LIPS!

Every so often, a young starlet comes along with something on her face that really stands out ... No not her nose, I'm talking about big, juicy lips. The type of lips you could use as a pillow. So many women try and fake the full-lipped look (and end up looking like a fish in a wig) but these women need no help in the mouth department whatsoever. They don't even need lip liner, for crying out loud!

But instead of crying "IT'S NOT FAIR!" and booking yourself in with the nearest trout-pout doctor, just accept that some ladies have luscious lips and some don't.

These women here may have lips to die for, but they're probably lacking in some other department ... okay so they're not lacking in anything, I'm just trying to make my little lips feel less inadequate here okay?

I give these ladies
a lip-smacking
/ 10

KEIRA KNIGHTLEY

Keira Knightley is spoilt positively rotten when it comes to dressing up.
If she's not looking elegant whenever there's red carpet about, she's wearing
the most exquisite gowns in illustrious films.

Anna Karenina is one of those films.

In it, Keira (who plays a water-eyed harlot) gets to drink tea and read,
while other people dress her in layer upon layer of richly coloured satin.

The story is set in a vodka-fuelled 19th-century Russia, where Anna and
Vronsky share looks and lingering glances before falling in love during what
we can only describe in modern-day language as a "dance-off". The problem
is that she is married to a very grumpy Jude Law, who does not take kindly
to his wife running off with someone who has a better moustache than him.

Things I learned whilst watching *Anna Karenina*:

(1) It IS possible to look chic when it is really cold outside. Rather than
waking up and putting on all your clothes, try furry hats and stoles instead.

(2) Speed dating also existed in 19th-century Russia, albeit with alphabet
building blocks.

(3) If you enjoy 2 hour 9 minute-long perfume commercials,
you'll love *Anna Karenina*.

I give Keira Knightley an exquisite

BRITNEY SPEARS

Even after all these years
It's still okay to love Britney Spears
and even after all the tears
And her famous run-in with hair shears
She's still like music to the ears
Performing to applause and cheers

When "Toxic" comes on the radio
There's just something you should know:
Your dignity away you'll throw
And sing along like you're at the show
Its catchy riff will grow and grow
It will get in your head and never go

OH NO!

Oops! I scored Britney  /10

'70s SPECIAL

DIANE KEATON
Annie Hall, 1977, Dir. Woody Allen

Diane ... /10

Previously known for her role in *The Godfather* and *The Godfather: Part II*, Diane Keaton showed her true potential as an adlibbing comedy actress with impeccable timing in Woody Allen's *Annie Hall*.

Annie Hall is a romantic comedy revolving around Alvy Singer (Woody Allen) and Annie Hall (Diane Keaton). Like many Woody Allen films, it is set against a New York backdrop and Allen's neuroses.

Annie Hall is a charming, laid back and slightly ditsy character, but with an impeccable sense of style. When the couple first meet, Annie Hall is all about "the boyfriend look" with boyfriend chinos, boyfriend shirt and tie and maybe a girlfriend's boyfriend waistcoat. It was a truly iconic look that has stood the test of time, and has been emulated by Meg Ryan in *You've Got Mail*, among many others.

MERYL STREEP
Kramer vs Kramer, 1979, Dir. Robert Benton

Meryl ... /10

Kramer vs Kramer is a film that makes me sob even more than *The Notebook* does.
If you have yet to see this film and don't enjoy crying in public, WATCH IT ALONE ...
with many, many tissues.

Meryl Streep plays a smartly dressed mother in typical late '70s style, feminine blouses with knee-length skirts, slouchy boots and long rain macs. Streep began her acting career shortly before *Kramer vs Kramer* and has since become one of the world's best-loved actresses.

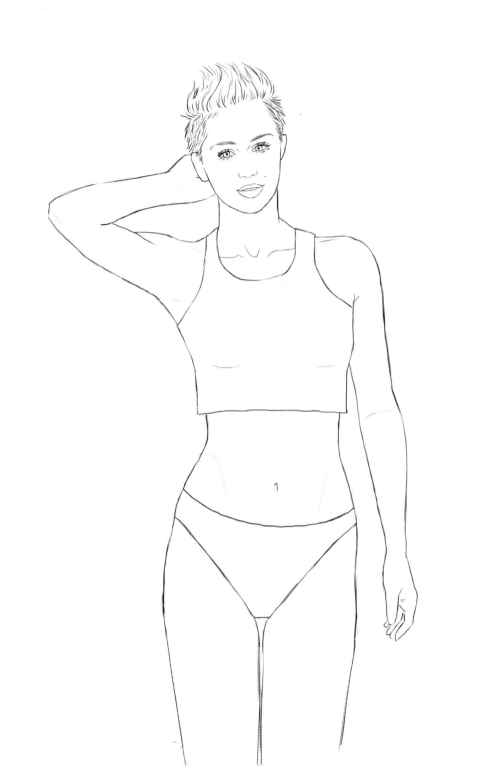

MILEY CYRUS

At the time of writing, Miley Cyrus is 20 years old and has just won the MTV EMA award for Best Video, for "Wrecking Ball". Obviously, the press are not focusing on her win, or her brilliantly shot video (by renowned fashion photographer Terry Richardson) to a brilliantly sung record – they are instead focusing on her twerking with a dwarf, and Miley's lack of outfit while accepting her award.

Beginning her fame as child pop star Hannah Montana, Miley (a nickname short for "smiley") has broken away from her cutesy Disney image and is concentrating on a more independent music career. She is quickly establishing herself as a wild force to be reckoned with, quite rightly realising that, in an industry full of young pop starlets, she needs to stand out. And she does ... by a mile.

After growing up portraying the perfect pop star, it's understandable that she would wish to sever her ties with Miss Montana and her Dad's achy breaky heart. She is young, and like all young people, she'll probably do or wear things that will make herself cringe in a few years to come, but c'mon, who hasn't!?

I score Miley a super-smiley / 10

KIRSTEN DUNST

I am pretty certain that Sofia Coppola's brilliantly decadent film *Marie Antoinett*e started the worldwide trend for pugs and coloured macaroons.

If you haven't yet seen the film, with its romantic storyline and indie soundtrack, think of it as *Made in Chelsea* set during the French Revolution (and think of *Les Misérables* as *TOWIE* if we're doing the whole comparison thing).

Kirsten Dunst and her adorable dimples portrayed Marie Antoinette as delightful and charming. Fond of coloured cakes and champagne, she brought clapping back and had a bit of ooh-la-la with Jamie Dornan. Marie Antoinette was obviously very popular with the people around her – but not so much with the malnourished French commoners who didn't have so much as a petit four between them.

The Oscar-winning costumes by Milena Canonero really are about as opulent as you can get, with pastel colours, bows, ribbons and more corsets than you can shake an éclair at!

Fantastique!

I give Kirsten a fancy French  10

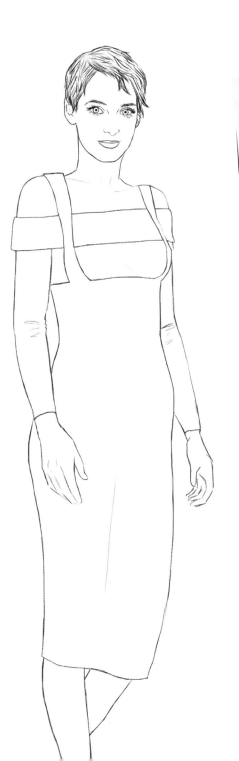

WINONA RYDER

Best '90s Moments
Reality Bites, Mermaids, Edward Scissorhands, Dracula, Girl, Interrupted, Little Women, Celebrity.

10

SHERILYN FENN

Best '90s Moment

As super sultry Audrey Horne in David Lynch TV drama, *Twin Peaks*.

/10

NAOMI CAMPBELL

Best '90s Moments
George Michael "Freedom '90"
video, falling with grace during
Vivienne Westwood's catwalk show.

/10

PAMELA ANDERSON

Best '90s Moments
Baywatch, Home Improvement,
Barb Wire.

/10

CAITLIN MORAN

When plasterer Matt Cardle (* Google him) was taking part in *The X Factor* 2011, and I read the tweet, "He could make my face look like a plasterer's radio anyday!" I literally LOL-ed, and let me assure you, I'm not a big LOL-er, LOL-ing is just not my thing.

While I love Caitlin's book *How to Be a Woman*, and her regular columns for *The Times*, it's **@caitlinmoran** who gets my vote.

I follow umpteen comedic megastars, but there is no other person on Twitter who is as brutally honest, self-depreciating and downright hilarious as Caitlin Moran. With quick-witted wisecracks (that are often so quick that Caitlin probably gets the sort of whiplash that has Injury Lawyers 4U banging on her door), she often embarrasses herself. But it's exactly this embarrassment, unrivalled honesty and filthy sense of humour that have gained her close to half a million followers.

If you don't yet follow @caitlinmoran, do ... and then follow @mellyelliott and thank me for the recommendation.

I score Caitlin a whopping  /10

* Okay, don't ACTUALLY Google him, I already told you that he was a plasterer and that he took part in *The X Factor* 2011, what else do you need to know? Oh, he won by the way.

AMY POEHLER & AUBREY PLAZA

If any TV show made me want to have a BFF, who I would share my wine and good times with, *Parks and Recreation* is it ... and the BFF is Leslie Knope (played by Amy Poehler).

Leslie Knope is the enthusiastic mid-level member of the Parks and Recreation department of Pawnee, Indiana, and April Ludgate (played by Aubrey Plaza) is a lethargic young intern in the same department. Together they are pure comedy joy in one of the best shows for a long time (in my opinion). If you haven't seen *Parks and Recreation*, do check it out.

If you worked for Pawnee Parks Department, who would be your BFF, Leslie or April?

I give Amy Poehler  and Aubrey Plaza

SARAH JESSICA PARKER

So I'm sitting here in my Manola Blahniks* working on my MacBook, trying to channel a Carrie Bradshaw column, but then I couldn't help but wonder: "Can you write a page of unanswered questions and still get any kind of point across?"

Carrie Bradshaw, the lead character in *Sex And The City*, was a newspaper columnist who seemed clueless about life, adulthood and relationships – but she looked FANTASTIC as she wondered and pondered her way through it.

Sex And The City, written by Candace Bushnell, told the story of four female friends, each one with her own set of baggage and hang-ups, and each with their own style. Time after time I would tick my way through a "Which Member of *Sex And The City* Are You Most Like?" magazine quiz, only to be mortified that I wasn't Carrie (I still think I'm most like Carrie by the way, all the quizzes were wrong).

Women worldwide lapped up the show season after season. Its honesty was reassuring and sometimes empowering and its wardrobe department, created by Patricia Field, was outstanding.

I have depicted Sarah Jessica Parker opposite, as Carrie Bradshaw, wearing the pink Oscar de la Renta gown given to her by "The Russian".

SJP scores /10

* I'm not really wearing Manolo Blahniks, I'm actually weraring a pair of grey socks, they are inside out and there is a hole in each one where my red chipped toenail polish is on display. I just took a photograph of them.

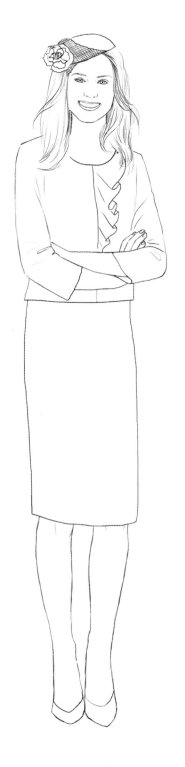

KATE MIDDLETON

Or, of course, HRH The Duchess of Cambridge, as we should now call her. The whole world seems to absolutely love the often serenely smiling Duchess, and since her engagement to Prince William, events in her life have frequently brought everything to a standstill – millions of us tuned in to watch her wedding and the announcement of the birth of Prince George. And with that wedding she married into a family of incredible hat enthusiasts. Whether it's the odd contraption Princess Beatrice wore for Kate's wedding, or the succession of rather less flashy round hats and matching pastel suits the Queen wears to her numerous appearances, the Royal Family's women display a parade of interesting head gear.

Of course Royal fashion is usually much more traditional: the Queen has her winning formula and quite possibly a suit of similar style with matching hat in every single shade known to mankind. Meanwhile Kate is a patron of many labels, picking stylish yet sensible and flattering clothes … And makes it look so easy that her style has been endlessly imitated, and as I write shops are stocking up on fancy little "fascinators" to pin in your hair in the style of her miniature, side-slanted hats.

I give Princess Kate a right royal 10

BRIDESMAIDS

Bridesmaids is the 2011 film directed by Paul Feig, following the lives of a bride-to-be and her friends as they prepare for the big day.

Starring (from left to right) Kristen Wiig, Maya Rudolph, Melissa McCarthy and Rose Byrne, it is undoubtedly one of the funniest films I have seen, with one cringe-worthy incident after another, each one resonating with me in some way.

Melissa McCarthy's performance is outstanding, so much so that, having seen *Bridesmaids* several times, I have only just realised that she is Molly from *Mike and Molly*!

If you haven't seen this film yet, watch it with your girlfriends (that is if you don't mind them seeing you literally rolling on the floor laughing).

I give the
Bridesmaids
a side-splitting 10

TYRA BANKS

I don't know about you but I LOVE modelling competitions
(I also love singing competitions, baking competitions and any
other competition that makes me cry whilst watching the TV).

Whenever I hear Tyra say the words "I'm sorry but you are no
longer in the running to be America's Next Top Model" I am
utterly heartbroken ... but then I realise that (A) I never entered
the competition because, (B) I'm not American, (C) I'm too old
to enter the competition even if I were American, (D) My legs
are at least 12 inches too short, (E) I have wonky "British teeth"
and (F) I hate having my photograph taken. But other than that
I'm sure I could be in the running to be America's Next Top
Model! Hell yeah!

I adore seeing unconfident, average-looking girls eventually
strutting their stuff, realising how amazing they are, becoming
powerful and confident, and learning to embrace what they
previously regarded as their faults.

I also adore how Tyra Banks always looks so "fierce"
and amazing.

I give Tyra a fierce

/10

JENNIFER LOPEZ

When Jennifer Lopez wore a dazzling green Versace dress with a neckline that plunged and plunged and then plunged a bit more, she quickly became "Jenny With the Frock".

Puff Diddy Whatsisname tried desperately to outshine her in his white suit that was probably made from recycled super-yachts. But he failed, miserably.

The dress was sheer with a tropical print. The neckline went all the way past Jen's belly button and the split in the front of the floor-length gown went all the way up to meet it. Jen looked sensational and was most definitely the talk of the party (not that I was there or anything, I'm just guessing here, I never get invited anywhere).

Jennifer Lopez was not only responsible for showing us that plunging necklines make headlines, she also put fear into boyfriends and husbands everywhere, as the question "Does my bum look big in this?", now had two possible answers!

I give Jen a bootylicious

10

LINDSAY LOHAN

As you have probably gathered by now, I am far from perfect. I make mistakes just like everyone else, sometimes huge ones too. Sometimes I even make them in public, but I just pick myself up and continue like nothing has happened. I'm not entirely sure if I could do this if, each time I messed up, it was displayed on the front of numerous newspapers and magazines – with editors just waiting for me to mess up again and again so they have something juicy to print.

Having modelled and acted in TV commercials from the age of three, Lindsay Lohan shot to fame at the very young age of 12, starring alongside herself in *The Parent Trap*. With her red hair, freckles and cheeky charisma, audiences loved her. Fame and fortune, however, did not.

If you're one of the "Mean Girls" who judges and berates Lindsay each time she makes a mistake, ask yourself how you would have handled all the fame and pressure at such a young age. Then maybe reconsider.

Lindsay scores 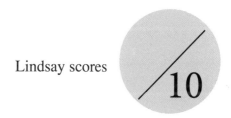 /10

TAYLOR SWIFT

What I love about Taylor Swift
Is the thing that gets some people miffed
She dates some boys and does collect
Their information for a song project

In doing this she often caters
To Internet douchebags and they're called "haterz"
But haterz are always gonna hate
So Taylor just goes on another date

I give Taylor the best score ever, ever, ever

/10

Audrey Hepburn has gone down in history as one of the most stylish and beautiful actresses. Remembered as an icon, she is usually pictured in her *Breakfast at Tiffany's* pearls and long cigarette holder. Her own choice was a more casual look: I'd imagine most actresses don't usually wear their Oscar ballgowns around the house!

Twiggy made her name as a model in the '60s for being stick-thin (if you were assuming the name was completely coincidental and nothing to do with her weight, you're wrong – but points for thinking outside the box!) and for having the biggest eyes ever to sit on a human face, an effect she achieved by layering on fake eyelashes and paint until she must hardly have been able to open her eyes. It worked, and she made being an awkward teenager attractive. She's still involved in fashion today, although without the sultry expression that made her famous.

ICONS SPECIAL

A trend-setting First Lady, before she became known as "Jackie O", Jackie Kennedy had a huge impact on fashion. After her husband's death, she continued to be an icon, switching to more casual styles. She popularised several looks, from big sunglasses and turtlenecks to the wool suit and pill-box hat combination she was wearing when JFK was assassinated … Her fashion choice then took a grisly turn, as she refused to take the suit off, and wore it for the swearing-in of Lyndon B. Johnson, still soaked in her husband's blood. Full respect to her, but … eww.

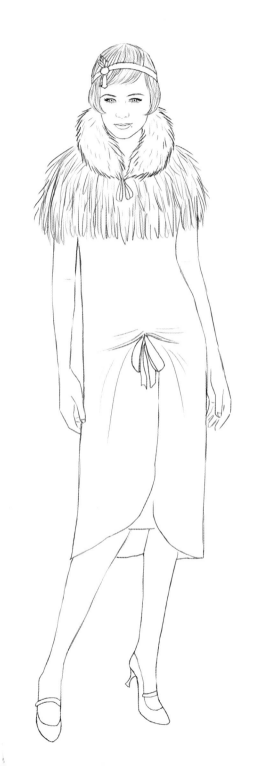

CAREY MULLIGAN

Carey Mulligan is quickly becoming a costume drama favourite, and no drama has more costumes than a Baz Luhrmann film. Appearing as the beautiful and stylish Daisy in his *Great Gatsby* adaptation, Carey Mulligan was the picture of 1920s flapper fashion. The actress often sports a cute pixie cut or other short style, following a disastrous run-in with peroxide for one of her earlier roles. Since then she has proved you don't need flowing hair to be adorable. In *The Great Gatsby* her bob, with its elegant curls at the front, defines her classy look.

Bedecked in millions of dollars worth of real diamonds for some scenes, she found herself closely watched in case she ran off with any of the Tiffany jewellery! Her dresses for the film were specially designed by Prada – again no expense spared – as were 40 of the dresses worn by mere extras in the background of the party scenes. Wouldn't it be fab to get your own personal designer dress just for dancing in the background of a film? Alas, the extras probably didn't get to keep them. Carey elegantly poses throughout the film in dresses made from lace or seemingly created out of petals, as well as typical 1920s shifts and demure headscarves.

It's not hard to love Carey, a sweet and determined actress … Although it is also easy to be jealous of anyone who gets to star as Leo DiCaprio's love interest!

Carey scores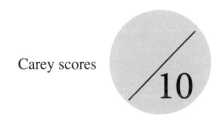

MICHELLE OBAMA

The First Lady makes a powerful statement with her fashionable style. Appearing beside her deeply cool husband, a President of the United States with a sense of humour, and who can sing too, you'd think she would have to work hard to shine, but with her colourful casual dresses or glamorous ballgowns, she leads the world in style. Literally!

Her dresses and pant suits have a unique and sometimes quirky style: as a First Lady and one-time lawyer you might have expected her to cut a dull, if respectable, figure, but she brings colour and flair to the job. And she absolutely rocked the look when she cut her hair into a fringe.

Another difference from across the pond is how cool the First Family are compared to any British politicians!

Michelle scores a mighty / 10

KYLIE MINOGUE

It's nice to have a little bum
Kylie should know 'cause she's got one
If your bum is tiny, this I have found
You just go to posh bars and spin round and round
The world went into envy hysteria
Of Kylie Minogue and her perfect posterior
Oh pop princess, you can sing, you can dance
And we salute you and your golden hot pants

I give Kylie a perfectly pert

/10

JENNIFER ANISTON

Gorgeous Jennifer Aniston came to our attention in 1994 as Rachel Green in *Friends*. Rachel was a spoilt rich girl, determined to be an independent woman with a job, a huge warehouse apartment, a circle of like-minded friends, a glamorous wardrobe and a HAIRCUT TO BEAT ALL HAIRCUTS!

Yes, since Jennifer Aniston's hair first appeared on our screens nearly 20 years ago, women in their thousands were walking the streets of this fine planet of ours, sporting what actually resembled a grown-out mullet, dubbed the "Rachel Cut".

If you want to recreate this classic haircut:

(1) Ask yourself why.
(2) Warn your friends and family.
(3) Take the diagram below to your hairdresser (who is probably too young to remember the "Rachel Cut").
(4) Do not hold me or Jennifer Aniston responsible for the results.

 Cut your hair into graduating lengths, like so, and then ...

 /10

I give Jen a super-layered

ADELE

Adele … The voice! No wait, the hair … No, it has to be the voice …
Man, it's hard to pick what is bigger and more fabulous about this beautiful
singer. No one's hair should have that much volume and curl, but hers does!
She looks like she has stepped out of another era with her retro beehives and smoky
eyeshadow … it's easy to forget how young she is, appearing on the scene when
she was just 19. What would you like to be famous for before you're even 20?

Adele can be as stormy as her lyrics. She's made her feelings known by giving
the finger to the camera on live TV when her Brit Awards acceptance speech was
cut short. She's also stood strong on her weight, claiming that she is happy as she
is and won't lose it unless it gets in the way of her life – a reassuring change of
pace from many stars who fear they'll be cast out into the cold for gaining
a single pound!

And now we should sit quietly and worry about just how much trouble would
be caused if she actually worked out how to set fire to the rain …

Adele gets a fabulous

10

CHLOË GRACE MORETZ

At the young age of 16, Chloë Grace Moretz is fast becoming one of the world's best-loved actresses.

She's hilarious as the sassy, wise-cracking little sister alongside Joseph Gordon-Levitt in *500 Days of Summer*, super-cute in *Diary of a Wimpy Kid*, super-vulnerable in *Hick* and super-kick-ass hero in ... er ... *Kick-Ass* (and *Kick-Ass 2*).

Chloë seems to have made a name for herself within the horror genre too, with *Let Me In*, *The Eye, Room Six, The Amityville Horror* and now scary schoolgirl *Carrie* all under her belt!

Chloë gets a kick-ass

10

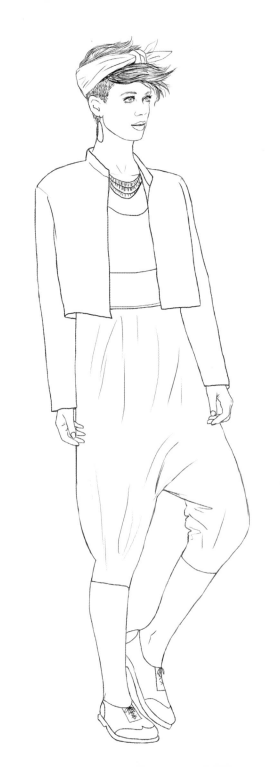

LISA BONET

An open letter to Lisa Bonet:

Dear Lisa,

Like many women, I would have given my right (and left) arm to be you in 1984. While everyone else was parading around in white stilettos and ra-ra skirts, you stepped away from the crowd, found a massively popular TV show to be on and used it flaunt your experimental, bohemian style. You were the coolest thing on the planet, hands down.

On behalf of fashionable women everywhere, I would like to say "Thank you". Without you (and your incredible talent for spotting trends, decades before anyone else does) ...

- We would only be able to buy brogues in men's sizes.
- The only people wearing headscarves would be old grannies.
- MC Hammer wouldn't have had any trousers on in his "You Can't Touch This" video. Eww!
- People don't run away in fear of girls with side-cuts anymore, 'cause you had one and you were really lovely and not scary in the slightest!

Thank you Lisa, from the botttom of my fashion-loving heart.

Love,

Mel x

I give Lisa a super-cool / 10

RACHEL McADAMS

The Notebook has to be the soppiest sob-fest of a film in the history of filmmaking. Anyone who can sit through this film without snivelling their way through a box of Kleenex needs to go straight to A&E to check if they actually have a heart.

Rachel McAdams plays Ally to Ryan Gosling's Noah. They play a couple of feisty young lovers who become separated and heartbroken due to parental intervention and that pesky romance-stopper they call "war".

Noah writes Ally a letter every day for a whole year, but she never gets them ... you can see where this is going, can't you?

Anyway, before I start welling up again, I picked Rachel McAdams in *The Notebook* because of her dainty 1940s tea dresses, headscarves and hats and gloves. It also gave me another opportunity to gaze at Ryan Gosling and claim it as "work".

If you were trying to make Baby Goose say YOU are some kind of animal, what would it be?

If Ryan's a 10, Rachel's a

10

TAVI GEVINSON

Tavi Gevinson started writing her fashion blog, entitled "Style Rookie", at the tender age of 12. She posted photographs of her tiny self in crazy outfits and she wrote about current trends, as well as how some of her favourite films and music had shaped her sense of fashion.

I started following Tavi when I became aware of her in 2009, intrigued about someone so young just "doing their thing", not conforming to teenage rules of what one should like and dislike and wear and watch. I was excited that someone that age was brave enough to be themselves ... not only that, but put it out there too, for the whole world to read (imagine letting ANYONE read your 13-year-old diary!).

I think of this as brave and intriguing because I remember being a young teenager, feeling completely insecure and just wanting to fit in. I didn't quite fit in but I'd have done anything to do so. It's difficult to not care about whether or not you fit in when you're 12 or 13 years old, even when, deep down you know it's what you should be doing.*

Tavi embraces this aspect of being a teenager, inspiring other girls her age to embrace what they love. She has spoken at many high-profile conventions but with a sense of modesty, not claiming to be a teenage genius or prophet, but just being into stuff, like any other teenage girl.

'Rookie' is an online magazine founded by Tavi in 2011, which has since sparked two yearbooks. It is an online portal for teenage girls, as well as being Tavi's (and other contributors') creative outlet. Whether you're a teenage girl, boy or just someone who wants a different opinion, do give it a read.

Tavi and the next two girls are far too cool to be marked out of 10

* The last two entries in this book are also girls who, at a very young age, have dared to step away from the crowd and be themselves.

LORDE

From listening to Lorde's songs I can only gather that, as a young girl, she watched films and shows such as *Heathers*, *Clueless*, *Mean Girls*, *The O.C.* and *My Sweet Sixteen*, and (like loads of us) felt that she didn't quite belong in that popular clique.

As with Tavi Gevinson, this is another young lady who has realised the stupidity of "fitting in" way before many of us mere mortals did.

Her astoundingly good lyrics speak sarcastically of dreaming of being the "Queen Bee" and talking on the tennis court "like yeah".

It's refreshing to see such a young woman being herself and writing about the apparently trivial dilemas faced by other girls her age.

Lorde just craves a different kind of buzz.

"ONE CHILD,
ONE TEACHER,
ONE BOOK,
AND ONE PEN,
CAN CHANGE THE
WORLD"

Malala Yousafzai 2013

MALALA YOUSAFZAI

Malala's story is one that inspires absolute horror: a teenager being shot by the Taliban for campaigning for education for girls, but it ends in hope, as Malala survived and is now a hugely influential public speaker, with plans to head into politics and try to address the problems that led to her assassination attempt.

We love Malala not just because she's brave and a survivor, but because she was already fighting hard before she was shot, and has only come out of it fighting harder for what she believes in. It's inspirational for every girl, and she's the sort of girl we should all really want to be.

So, next time you're thinking that your life would be better if only you had Kylie's bum, or if you had bigger breasts, or smaller thighs, longer eyelashes, fuller lips or clearer skin or those shoes you saw last week, stop fretting, accept yourself and think about something more important instead.

Think ... "What would Malala do?"

ABOUT MEL ELLIOTT

Rather than write some boring blurb about myself, I got my Facebook friends to ask me questions:

What started you on the whole colouring book thing?
I met a printer and fell in love. I was thinking of stuff he could print and ended up considering what I'd like to buy that I couldn't ... and a Kate Moss colouring book was the answer! This was in 2008, and it wasn't until 2009–10 that I considered it an actual job.

Have you ever used the British Embassy?
Yes. I got stuck in Milan once with no passport or money and had to survive on some stolen breadsticks and a bottle of brandy. The British Embassy were fantastic!

Have you ever met Shakin' Stevens?
No, but I did see him in concert in Blackpool once.

Have you ever snogged a celebrity?
While in Blackpool I bought a satin cushion with Shakin' Stevens' face on it. I used to snog that cushion … a lot.

Who is your ultimate girl/boy crush from the '80s and '90s?
'80s – I desperately wanted to look like Vanessa Paradis when I first witnessed "Joe le Taxi" and Michael J. Fox (once I was over my Shaky obsession).
'90s – Kate Moss and Noel Gallagher.

Who is your favourite member of One Direction?
Harry. I saw them live in Barcelona this year (on my own) with an open mind, but Harry stood out for me.

The socks from page 88

If you could take five things onto a desert island, what would they be?
A colouring book, my pencil case (which has an eraser and sharpener in it too), a kettle, some teabags and some matches.

Do you ever eat cold baked beans straight out of the tin?
ABSOLUTELY NOT! I shudder at the thought!

If you were DJ-ing, what three tracks would you play to fill the dancefloor?
"I Feel Love" by Donna Summer, "Harder, Better, Faster, Stronger" by Daft Punk and "Dancing With Myself" by Generation X.

What was the first ever *Colour Me Good* **image?**
It was a drawing of Kate Moss with her shoulder straps falling down, it's still one of my favourites and I have it pinned to my studio wall.

Please check out Mel's other books:
Colour Me Swooooon
and
1980s Bumper Activity Book
as well as her full range of colouring books and other gifts, at
www.ilovemel.me

Twitter: **@mellyelliott**

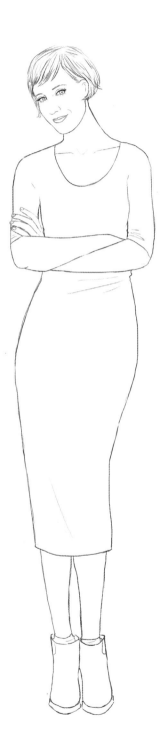

Also available

COLOUR ME SWOOOOON

Hotties, hunks, heartthrobs, beefcakes, dreamboats, studs. It doesn't matter what you call them, all that counts is that they make you go weak at the knees. But what are the chances of you getting up close and personal with David Beckham, Jake Gyllenhaal or Nicholas Hoult? Well, here is the next best thing…

Colour Me Swooooon allows you to caress the chiselled features of 60 of your favourite pieces of macho eye candy. From Aaron Paul to Zac Efron, all the guys are here and can't wait for you to come and give them a damn good colouring in!

So get your felt-tips ready and make Ryan Gosling's brooding face blush, run your fingers through George Clooney's silver hair, stare into Harry Styles' dreamy green eyes and – deep breath – touch up Bradley Cooper's abs!

COLOUR ME SWOOOOON

The heartthrob activity book for good colour-inners, as well as beginners

Mel Elliott

9781909396234